Mr. Lazy's Guide to
FIT

Written by Adam Hargreaves and Andrew Langley
Illustrated by Adam Hargreaves

MR MEN AND LITTLE MISS™
& © 2000 Mrs Roger Hargreaves. Printed and published in 2000
under licence from Price Stern Sloan Inc., Los Angeles.

Published in Great Britain by Egmont World Limited,
a division of Egmont Holding Limited,
Deanway Technology Centre, Wilmslow Road, Handforth,
Cheshire SK9 3FB, UK.

Printed in Italy

ISBN 0 7498 4891 X

THE REALISTIC RUNNING MACHINE

"It's Mr. Lazy's new strolling machine."

"Ever since I started exercising I've lost pounds. First there were the new trainers, and then the kit bag, and then the kit to go in the bag, and now ... the gym membership fee."

Mr. Mean

Mr. Rush's habit of running on the spot was proving to be something of a hazard.

Mr. Rush

Mr. Lazy discovered that he excelled at the deep breathing exercises.

"Touch my toes?"

Mr. Greedy

"Getting fit is all about mind over matter.
I don't mind, so it doesn't matter."

While running the marathon Mr. Bump came up against what all long distance runners dread - 'THE WALL'.

Select the apparatus which is
most suitable to your needs.

Mr. Small

Everyone has their ideal shape.

Mr. Happy   Mr. Strong   Mr. Rush

Mr. Happy

ADRENALIN RUSH

Mr. Rush

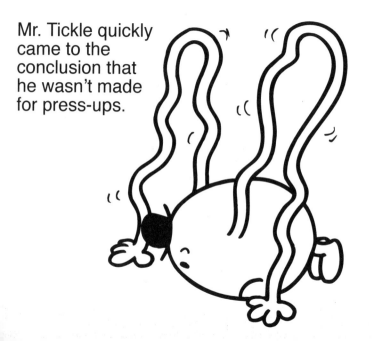

Mr. Tickle quickly came to the conclusion that he wasn't made for press-ups.

Nor was Mr. Greedy!

PUMPING IRON

Mr. Silly   Mr. Small

It was when
he looked in
the mirror that
Mr. Skinny
decided it
was time to
join a gym.

Mr. Small

WEIGHT TRAINING

Mr. Nonsense

"He kept falling off his exercise bike so we got him some stabilisers."

Mr. Bump

"He's into body sculpture."

"What?
Henry Moore."

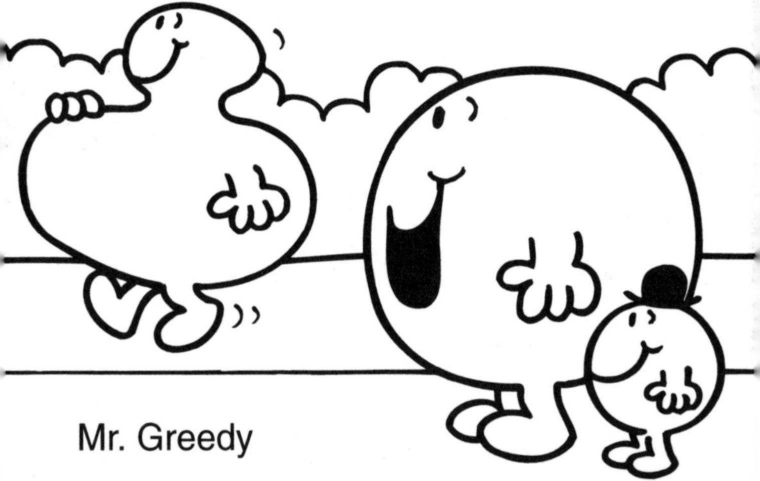

Mr. Greedy

Mr. Worry

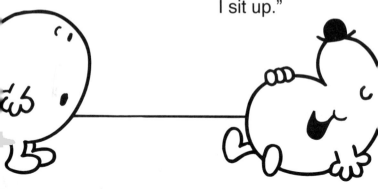

"Actually, I like to think of it as my Wealth Club."

Mr. Dizzy's personal trainer had told him to dig deep when he next went running.

Before he left for the gym Mr. Worry double checked his gym kit.

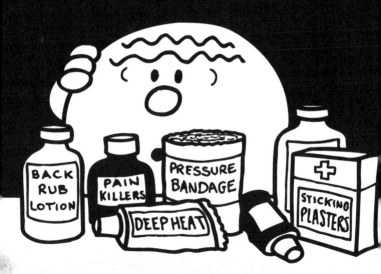

He forgot to breathe.

Mr. Forgetful

Little Miss Neat couldn't bring herself to do it. Just the thought of all that sweat.

Mr. Small

Mr. Wrong was puzzled.

He'd advertised all over town, but still no one had joined his new gym.

Mr. Sneeze presented some very unique challenges to his personal trainer.

Mr. Silly had personalised his exercise bike.

Little Miss Shy could work up
a sweat before she even got
to the gym.

Just the thought of all that lycra.

"What is that?"

"Mr. Tall's weights."

Every time Mr. Topsy-Turvy turned on the running machine the same thing happened.

Mr. Skinny couldn't help but feel rather smug every time he went to the gym.

Contrary to what he'd been told,
Mr. Forgetful had always found
weight-lifting surprisingly easy.

Little Miss Splendid goes into training before the sales start.

NO PAIN NO GAIN

Mr. Bump

Mr. Greedy proves Archimedes'
principle each time he gets into
the plunge pool.

Mr. Lazy understood the importance of
warming up properly before taking exercise.

Mr. Lazy picks a convenient date for exercising.

THE CURL